The Beginne Book of Cooking ɪor Arthritis

Alice Reynolds, S.E.N.

Preface

Two years ago I contracted arthritis; I was practically immobile. According to my GP's diagnosis, I was suffering from two cold shoulders, plus the arthritis; I could not raise my arms above my head, get into the bath or get on a bus. It was also difficult to dress and undress and turn over in bed. To reach up to kitchen shelves was an impossibility and, as I live alone, this made things very awkward. The doctor said that I must try to raise my arms or I would never be able to do it.

I managed by 'creeping' my hands up the door, using it as a support, until after a week or two I was able to reach the top of the door. This became a daily exercise, amongst others.

As I have always been a very active woman I was devastated when the diagnosis was made. I went home, made a cup of tea and sat down to think – walking sticks, wheel chairs, medication, injections all came to mind.

I visited the local library to find out more and was fortunate to come across a book by a Chinese-American doctor, named Colin Dong. He was also suffering from arthritis and a very nasty form of dermatitis. He remembered what his father had said to him, that 'poison goes in through the mouth and catastrophe comes out of the mouth' and created a non-allergenic diet to see if it would help. He used the sorts of things he had eaten as a child, mainly fish, rice and vegetables. He was amazed that, after only a few weeks, things improved dramatically. He was eventually able to play golf again and lead a normal life.

My own experience, after only 6 weeks of following the diet, was that I was able to dress myself more easily and the 'early morning stiffness' that I had experienced, was clearing earlier each day. I was able to get in and out of a car, in and out of bed and I am now, once again, fully mobile and pain free.

This diet is not a cure. I am relieved that it has worked for me but, in the same way as a doctor may prescribe the same medication for two patients, it may work well for one but not for the other.

Do, however, try and persevere; it make take a longer or shorter time for you, but in the long term I'm convinced that you will see an improvement in your mobility. If you are on prescribed medication from your doctor, do not stop taking this.

I do not suggest that you eat **only** fish, rice and vegetables but these ingredients do form part of my diet. I hope this compilation of recipes will make the diet more interesting and varied.

I WISH YOU EVERY SUCCESS

ALICE REYNOLDS

Coping with Arthritis

Objectives

Decrease Pain   **Increase Mobility**

This diet will help you achieve the above objectives. Certain foods are restricted but I have provided substitutes where necessary. It is not as fearsome as a first glance might suggest and becomes a way of life after a while.

- **NO Dairy Products** (e.g. milk, cheese, butter, cream, yoghurt)
  Substitute – Soya milk, Soya spread, Soya cheese, Soya yoghurt

- **NO Red Meat or Animal Fat**
  Substitute – chicken, fish (particularly oily fish such as herring and mackerel), tuna in oil and shellfish

- **NO Chocolate**
  Substitute – carob (obtainable at health food shops)

- **NO Bovril, Oxo or Stock Cubes**
  Substitute – Marmite

- **NO Wheat (read the cereal packet)**
  Substitute – Rice Barley or Oats

PERMITTED

- All fresh fruit and some tinned
- All vegetables, fresh or frozen
- Oils such as olive and sunflower oil. (Some cooking oils are a mixture and should be avoided)
- TREX is a vegetable fat which takes the place of lard
- Turkey (not sausages as they contain fat)
- Egg White (this is where the protein is – the yolk is a ball of fat). Egg white can be used for cooking, e.g. pancakes – whisk well and add ½ teaspoon baking powder to batter mix
- Drinks - Rum, Vodka, Whisky and I think beer as they are all vegetable based. An occasional glass of white wine is good but NOT red as the grape skins are acidic. Fresh fruit juice and Soda water are very refreshing but I avoid bottled soft drinks as they contain sugar and often additives. Tea and coffee are OK

It will take approximately 6 weeks before any improvement is likely to be noticeable, but it will come if you persevere.

GOOD LUCK

ALICE REYNOLDS

Cooking Measurements

1 teaspoon (tspn) = 5ml

1 dessertspoon (dspn) = 10ml

3 teaspoons (tspn) = 1 tablespoon (tbspn) = 15ml = ½ fl oz.

2 tablespoons (tbspn) = 30ml = 1fl oz.

Metric (grams/Kgs)	Imperial (oz/lbs)
25g	1oz
50g	2oz
75g	3oz
100g	4oz = ¼lb
125g	<5oz
150g	>5oz
175g	6oz
200g	7oz
225g	8oz = ½lb
250g	9oz
275g	10oz
300g	11oz
325g	<12oz = ¾lb
350g	>12oz
375g	13oz
400g	14oz
425g	15oz
450g	16oz = 1lb
675g	22oz = 1½lb
1Kg	2.2lb
1.2Kg	2½lb
1.3Kg	3lb
1.8Kg	4lb
2.2Kg	5lb

Metric (ml/L)	Imperial (fl oz/pts)	US Cups	US Pints
30ml	1 fl.oz.	$1/8^{th}$	
60ml	2 fl.oz.	¼	
90ml	3 fl.oz.		
120ml	4 fl.oz	½	¼ US pt
150ml	5 fl.oz = 1/4pt		
180ml	6 fl.oz.	¾	
210ml	7 fl.oz.		
240ml	8 fl.oz	1	½ US pt
270ml	9 fl.oz		
300ml	10 fl.oz. = ½pt	1¼	
330ml	11 fl.oz.		
360ml	12 fl.oz	1½	¾ US pt
390ml	13 fl.oz.		
420ml	14 fl.oz.	1¾	
450ml	15 fl.oz. = 3/4pt		
480ml	16 fl.oz.	2	1 US pt
600ml	20 fl.oz. = 1pt	2½	
960ml	32 fl.oz.	4	1 quart
1.1L	40 fl.oz. = 2pts	5	2½ US pts

Oven Temperatures

Degrees Fahrenheit	Degrees Celsius	Gas Mark	Description
225	110	¼	Very slow
250	120/130	½	Very slow
275	140	1	Slow
300	150	2	Slow
325	160/170	3	Moderate
350	180	4	Moderate
375	190	5	Moderately hot
400	200	6	Moderately hot
425	220	7	Hot
450	230	8	Hot
475	240	9	Very hot

Soya Milk

Soya milk is the alternative to dairy milk and must be used as a substitute in the diet. It is easily obtainable from most supermarkets and can be used in a variety of ways.

- Soya milk warmed and laced with a spoonful of honey is an excellent bedtime drink.
- Drink in tea or coffee, milk in first. (In coffee it will separate if the water is too hot or the coffee is too strong).
- Soya milk does not like to be microwaved except in cooked dishes but can be used in a saucepan to make custard, scrambled egg whites sauces or milk pudding.
- Soya milk will keep for years in an unopened carton but should be refrigerated after opening where it will keep for at least a week. As the carton becomes less full, give it a gentle shake, as there is a certain amount of sediment at the bottom.

Tofu

Tofu is a very useful alternative to meat; it is made of Soya beans and, as it is bland, needs a fair amount of spice to make it tasty. It comes in various forms but I buy a block of plain white Tofu and can then fry or poach it. Well spiced, it is good with a salad, especially with prawns, fried with tomatoes, egg white, and mushrooms, and can make a filling breakfast.

Soups

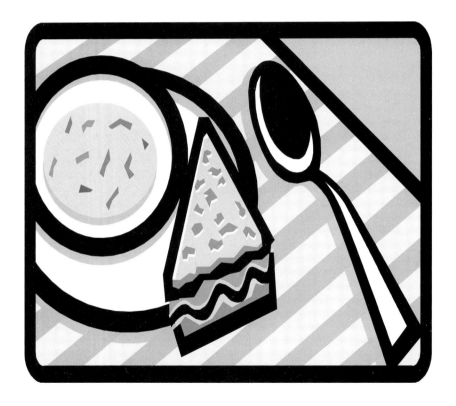

Chicken Stock

To use good soup stock is better than water. On this diet, stock cubes are not advisable as they contain animal fat and undesirable additives. Marmite is a good flavour enhancer and is cheaper than stock cubes: so here goes for Chicken Stock.

When you have finished your chicken, don't throw the carcass away; break it up, put it in a saucepan with a peeled onion, a bay leaf, and 2 pints of water. Simmer for 1 hour, strain, and cool. When cold, skim off any fat.

This stock will freeze.

Pumpkin Soup

Hallowe'en

A good, warming pumpkin soup is ideal for Hallowe'en when people come in from their Tricking & Treating. It doesn't have to be Hallowe'en though…

3lb pumpkin
1 medium potato
1 medium onion
3 egg whites
1½ltrs water
2 tbspn Soya spread
½ pt Soya milk
chopped chives
salt & pepper

Peel and cube the pumpkin and potato and finely chop the onion. Cook in a deep pan with salt and pepper to taste. Bring to the boil then reduce the heat and simmer for 18-20 minutes and drain. Pass through a fine sieve to puree. Return to a clean pan and add the Soya spread. Beat the egg white in a separate bowl, add the milk and stir until blended. Gradually add the egg white and milk to the pumpkin puree, stirring until thick and creamy. Serve sprinkled with chives.

Borscht

4 large cooked beetroot

2 tbspn Soya spread

1 large onion, chopped

Grated rind of 1 lemon

1 tbspn lemon juice

1 litre chicken stock

2 tspn sugar

⅔ cup tomato puree

2 egg whites

salt & pepper

Peel the beetroot and grate or chop finely. Melt the Soya spread in a deep pan and sauté the onion for 2-3 minutes until soft. Add the lemon juice, lemon rind and cover and simmer for 6-8 minutes. Add the beetroot, chicken stock, salt & pepper, and tomato purée then simmer for a further 5-6 minutes.

Beat the egg whites in a bowl and gradually stir in ½ a cup of hot soup until blended. Stir this mixture back into the soup and serve hot, or well chilled from the refrigerator.

Potato and Leek Soup

(Prince Charles' favourite Soup)

1lb peeled potatoes

4 good sized, well washed leeks

2 ozs Soya spread

2 pts vegetable stock

salt and pepper

Dice the potatoes and cut the leeks into ½ inch pieces. Sweat the leeks in the Soya spread and add the diced potatoes and vegetable stock. Bring to the boil and simmer until the potatoes have broken down. Add salt and pepper to taste.

Mushroom Soup

1 medium onion

2 ozs Soya spread

2 ozs self-raising flour

1½ pts chicken stock

4 ozs button mushrooms

½ pt Soya milk

salt and pepper

Finely chop the onion and sweat it in the Soya spread, in a pan, until transparent.

Slowly add the flour and hot chicken stock, stirring constantly to avoid lumps. Slice the mushrooms and add to the soup. Boil for 1 minute and season to taste.

Scotch Broth

2 ozs pearl barley

2 ozs marrowfat peas

2 pts chicken stock

1 large carrot and an equal weight of swede

1 large onion

2 leeks

2 ozs cabbage or kale

2 ozs Soya spread

1 tbspn chopped parsley

salt and pepper

Soak peas and pearl barley overnight, drain and wash. Add to the chicken stock and simmer for 1 hour. Grate or finely chop the vegetables and add to the broth together with the Soya spread. Simmer for a further hour, or until the peas are tender. Serve sprinkled with chopped parsley.

The above recipe serves 4-6. If made thick enough to stand a spoon up in and with a hunk of bread, it is a filling lunch, which can be reheated the following day for about 10 minutes before serving.

Doris's Fish Soup

Any fish except mackerel, herring, or salmon, as these are too oily.

½ lb fish

1 large carrot

1 tbspn vegetable oil

1 small onion

6 mint leaves, finely chopped

¼ tspn salt

1pt fish stock

1 clove garlic

2 large sprigs parsley, finely chopped

To make the stock, cut the fish into 3 or 4 pieces and put into a pan containing 1pt of water. Boil for 20 minutes then sieve and discard the fish.

Peel and slice the carrots and put into l/4pt water, cook until soft and puree. Slice and fry the garlic in oil until soft. Add the onion, fry until soft then add the herbs. Finally mix together with the fish stock.

Smoked Haddock Chowder

Chowder is a substantial soup.

1lb smoked haddock fillet

1lb peeled potatoes

1 large onion

2 ozs Soya spread

1 tbspn flour

½ cup Soya milk

1 tbspn chopped parsley

cream crackers and salt

Cover the haddock with water and cook. Cut potatoes and onions into ½ inch dice and sweat in the Soya spread, stir in the flour. Add the liquid the haddock was cooked in and enough water to cover the potatoes. Cook until tender. Break the haddock into bite-sized pieces and mix into the soup. Whiten with a little Soya milk, season and sprinkle parsley on the top. Serve with crackers.

Potato and Carrot Soup

1lb peeled potatoes

2 large carrots

1 large onion

2 ozs Soya spread

2 pts of any stock

salt and pepper

Dice the potatoes into ½ inch cubes. Grate or finely shred the carrots and roughly chop the onion. Sweat the onion in the Soya spread then add potatoes, carrots and stock. Cook until the potatoes have broken down. Season with salt and pepper.

Chicken Dishes

Sweet and Sour Chicken

2 tbspn light soy sauce

2 tbspn rice wine or sherry

2 cloves of garlic, crushed

1 inch piece of root ginger, peeled and finely grated

1lb chicken cut into 1-inch cubes

1 tbspn cornflour

2 tbspn rice vinegar

2 tbspn tomato sauce

1 red pepper, deseeded and diced

1 yellow pepper, deseeded and diced

6 ozs mange tout, topped and tailed

3 tbspn clear honey

2 tbspn vegetable oil

Mix the soy sauce, rice wine or sherry, garlic and ginger into a bowl. Add the chicken and cover and marinate in the fridge for one hour. Drain the chicken in a sieve, preserving the marinade. Add the cornflour, rice vinegar, tomato sauce and honey to the marinade and stir well. Heat 1 tbspn of vegetable oil in a frying pan or wok and add the chicken, stir frying over a high heat for 5 minutes. Remove the chicken from the pan with a slotted spoon and heat the remaining oil in the pan. Add peppers and mange tout and stir-fry over a high heat for 2 minutes. Add the marinade mixture to the pan and stir until thickened. Add the chicken and cook for 1 further minute, stirring constantly. For a fruity variation, add a can of pineapple chunks, in natural juice, to the chicken.

Chicken and Vegetable Salad

½ a small cauliflower

4 ozs thinly sliced carrots

4 ozs frozen green beans

2 ozs peas

4 ozs tinned sweet corn

1 celery stick, chopped finely

4 ozs diced cooked chicken with the skin removed

chopped parsley to garnish

Break the cauliflower into florets and cook with carrots, beans and peas in boiling water for 5 minutes (until al dente). Strain and stir all the vegetables together in a bowl and add the diced cooked chicken. Pour over some diet salad cream, toss well and serve garnished with chopped parsley.

Mushroom Stuffed Chicken with Sauce

1 Chicken

6 ozs sliced mushrooms

A finger of bread smeared with Marmite

salt and pepper

Wash and clean the chicken inside and cut a slit in the top. Stuff with the mushrooms and a finger of bread smeared with Marmite for extra flavour (if desired). Place in a baking tin and cover with foil. Cook in a preheated, moderate oven until cooked through and the juices run clear.

Sauce

1 tin chopped tomatoes

Basil, dried or fresh, to taste

1 clove of garlic, crushed

½ oz Soya spread

Melt the Soya spread in a small saucepan and add the crushed garlic. Cook for about 3 minutes then add the tomatoes and cook on a low heat until reduced. Pour the sauce over the chicken and sprinkle with chopped parsley to serve.

Chicken and Mushroom Pasties

1 onion, peeled and chopped

2 tbspn oil

8 ozs peeled potatoes

1 clove of garlic, crushed

4 ozs chopped, cooked chicken

8 ozs washed and chopped mushrooms

1 tbspn chopped parsley

Make 8 ozs of short crust pastry. For the filling, fry the onion in a little oil for 5 minutes then add the potato and garlic. Cook gently for a further 10 minutes, add the mushrooms and fry for 4-5 minutes. Add the chopped parsley, season and allow to cool. Pre-heat the oven to 200°C / 400°F (Gas mark 6). Divide the pastry into 4 equal pieces and roll each piece into a 6" diameter circle. Spoon a ¼ of the mixture, plus a portion of the chopped, cooked chicken, onto each pastry then moisten the edges and press together. Make a couple of steam holes in each pasty, and brush each one with a little Soya milk. Place on a baking tray and cook for 20-25 minutes or until golden brown.

These pasties freeze well.

Chicken Chasseur

8 chicken thighs or 4 breasts, coat with ½ tbspn flour and ½ tbspn oil

1 large chopped onion

2ozs sliced mushrooms

1 small tin tomatoes, chopped

1 cup chicken stock

lemon juice

Skin the chicken, coat in flour and brown in the oil. Remove and set aside. Add remaining flour to the oil, and cook to a nut brown. Add the onions, tomatoes and mushrooms, stir in the chicken stock and lemon juice. Season, simmer for a few minutes, add the chicken, and simmer for 20 minutes or until tender. Serve sprinkled with chopped parsley.

Turkey Goulash

1 ½ lbs turkey thighs skinned and chopped

2 tbspn oil

1 large onion, chopped

1 clove garlic crushed

1 tbspn flour

½ tspn tomato puree

pinch chilli powder

½ pt stock

Brown the turkey in the oil, add the onion and garlic and sweat until transparent. Stir in the flour and paprika, mix in the tomato and stir out any lumps. Season with salt and chilli, and bring it to the boil, add a little water or stock and simmer until the turkey is tender.

Fish Recipes

Herby Haddock

4 large fillets of fresh haddock

3 tbspn corn oil

1 tbspn white wine

1 tbspn chopped fresh parsley

½ tspn salt

½ tspn dried thyme

1 bay leaf

1 small pink onion, sliced

Place the haddock in a shallow dish. Combine the oil, water, salt and herbs and with this, marinade the fish. Sprinkle the onion over and add the bay leaf. Cover and leave in the fridge for 4 hours. Drain and cook under a pre-heated grill. During cooking, brush fillets with marinade.

Salmon Savouries

8 slices brown bread

2 ozs Soya spread

A small tin salmon or tuna

salt

2 egg whites

oil for frying

cucumber for garnish

Remove the crusts from the bread, cover each slice with Soya spread and sandwich the slices together with the mashed salmon or tuna. Cut each sandwich into 4 triangles. Beat the egg whites until just broken. Heat some oil in a frying pan then dip the sandwiches in the egg white and fry until golden brown. Drain on kitchen paper and garnish with cucumber.

For 1 serving halve the ingredients.

(I chopped the cucumber, and added mashed potatoes with the 4 triangles, making a very adequate lunch).

Fish Hash

1 tbspn oil

1 medium onion, finely chopped

1lb white fish, e.g. cod, coley (thoroughly defrost, if frozen) and cut into small pieces

12 ozs potato, cooked and diced

2 tomatoes, skinned and chopped

1 tbspn dried parsley

Heat the oil in a heavy bottomed pan and cook the onion until transparent but not brown. Add the fish, potatoes, tomatoes, and half of the parsley.

Mix thoroughly and press into a 'cake'. Cook on a low heat for 30 to 40 minutes until hash is browned underneath.

Cut into wedges and serve with peas, baked beans, or a green vegetable.

Mackerel

A good, oily fish, cheap and tasty – it may be grilled whole or filleted. To grill whole, cut three deep slashes across the back, roll in flour and season with turmeric and salt. Brush with oil and grill for about 6-7 minutes on each side. If filleted, grill for about 5 minutes each side. Serve with mustard or parsley sauce.

Soused Mackerel

4 large or 8 small mackerel or herrings

A few peppercorns

I bay leaf and 1 medium onion

½ tspn salt

Equal quantities of vinegar and water, to cover

Gut, head and tail the fish (your fishmonger can do this for you). Pack the fish tightly in an ovenware dish, sprinkle with peppercorns and thinly sliced onion. Add the bay leaf. Season the vinegar and water and bring to the boil. Pour over the fish, cover with foil and bake in a moderate oven for 20 minutes. Cool in the liquor.

This is a good dish served hot, or cold with a salad.

Fish Cakes

½lb cooked fish

½lb boiled potato

1 oz Soya spread

salt and pepper

batter

4 oz flour

¼ pt water

Mash fish, potatoes and Soya spread together and add salt and pepper.   Shape the mixture into 4 cakes and cool thoroughly. Dust with flour and coat with batter then fry in hot oil.

Tinned fish can be used if well drained. I save the oil for frying. Salmon, added to a white sauce, makes a tasty dressing for plain cooked white fish.

A slice of pink onion, chopped and added raw to the fish cake mixture gives a tasty bite, and a little more flavour.

Batter: Mix the flour and water together to make a batter to coat the fish. Add a pinch of turmeric, if desired.

Smoked Haddock Kedgeree

350g undyed smoked haddock-this is brown, not dyed bright yellow.

2 eggs	2 tbspn olive oil
1 tspn cumin	1 tspn ground turmeric
225g basmati rice	5oz Soya spread
1 tspn medium curry powder	
1 small onion finely chopped	
1 tspn ground ginger	5cm fresh ginger root, finely grated
1 tspn tomato puree	2 tbspn chopped flat leaf parsley
2 tbspn sultanas	Salt and pepper

Simmer the haddock in a small, uncovered pan for 3-4 minutes. Drain, reserving the liquid for the sauce. When cool, flake the haddock, discarding skin and bone. Boil the eggs for 7-8 minutes, chop the whites and discard the yolks. Heat oil in a large pan and add rice, sultanas, cumin and curry powder. Pour in 900 ml of water, and boil steadily for 10 minutes, until the rice is tender. Melt the Soya spread in a frying pan, sauté the onion, ginger and turmeric, until softened. Stir in the tomato puree and cook for 2 minutes. Stir in the parsley and 3tbspn of the reserved poaching liquid to just heat through the salt and pepper. Fluff up the cooked rice, fold in the flaked haddock and drizzle the sauce over. Garnish with the chopped egg.

Sea Bass Fillets

A quick and easy mid-day meal. Your fishmonger will fillet the bass for you or you may be able to buy frozen. It is a fish with a delicate flavour, but adapts to all types of cooking methods.

Sea Bass Fillets with Tomato Salsa

4 fresh tomatoes, deseeded and chopped

1 red onion, chopped

1 garlic clove, chopped

4 tbspn olive oil

1 tspn fresh lime juice

1 tbspn chopped, fresh coriander

2 chopped spring onions

salt and pepper

Cook the fillets, skin side down, for 2-3 minutes in a dry pan then turn and cook on the other side. Cook the onions, garlic and spring onions in the oil until they are transparent, then add the lime juice. Pour over fish and top with the coriander.

Cajun Sea Bream

A similar fish to bass, which can be treated in the same way. This recipe is spicier than the salsa.

4 boned bream fillets
40g melted Soya spread
½ tspn dried oregano
½ tspn dried basil
½ tspn dried thyme
2½ tspn paprika
1 tspn cayenne pepper
salt

Cook fish fillets skin side down in a dry frying pan for 2-4 minutes then turn and cook on the other side. Pour the melted Soya spread over the fish together with the mixed spices and allow to stand, to absorb the flavours into the fish.

Pilchard Curry

This recipe is enough for 2-3 people but it is easy to make a smaller quantity.

2 medium sized onions
1 tbspn oil
1 tbspn curry powder
1 green pepper
2 sticks celery
1 tspn curry sauce
450gm tin pilchards in tomato sauce
1 tbspn water or white wine
pinch turmeric

Peel and chop the onions, heat the oil in the frying pan and fry the onions for 1 -2 minutes. Sprinkle in the curry powder, and fry gently until the onions are soft. Remove the core and seeds of the pepper, chop up the flesh and add to the pan. Stir in the curry sauce and salt. Tip the pilchards on top of the onion, rinse out the can with water or white wine and pour over the fish. Cover the pan and simmer until the fish is heated through. Serve with brown or white rice, flavoured with pinch of turmeric.

Cakes and Puddings

Eggs

As the yolk of the egg is not used in cooking in this diet, the raising agent is lost when the egg is separated and must be replaced.

Whisk an egg white lightly, add 1 tspn of baking powder, and a tspn of vinegar. This egg white can be used in a variety of dishes (e.g. pancakes, cakes and puddings), or whenever an egg is required in a recipe.

Mock Cream

1 oz cornflour

1 pt Soya milk

1 oz Soya spread

1 oz vanilla sugar

Blend the cornflour with a little of the milk, and put the rest on to boil. Pour the boiling Soya milk on to the cornflour stirring all the time. Return the mixture to the pan and cook for 2 minutes until very thick.

Cream together the Soya spread and vanilla flavoured sugar and beat until light and fluffy. Gradually beat in the cold cornflour mixture a little at a time until the mixture is again light and fluffy. To flavour sugar, put sugar in a jar with a vanilla pod, cover and leave overnight or use a few drops of vanilla essence.

Decorating Cream

2 ozs icing sugar

2 ozs Soya spread

½ pt cold custard or cornflour sauce

Beat sugar and Soya spread until light and fluffy; gradually beat in custard or cornflour sauce, 1 tspn at a time, until mixture is the consistency of whipped cream. This can now be piped or spread.

Egg-less Sponge.

6 ozs self raising flour	1 level tspn baking powder
3 ozs Soya spread	2 ozs sugar
1 level tbspn golden syrup	1½ pints Soya milk

Jam or mock cream, for filling.

Sift the flour and baking powder; cream the Soya spread, sugar, and golden syrup, until soft and light. Add a little flour, then a little liquid, continuing in this way until you have a smooth mixture. Grease and flour 2 x 7 inch sandwich tins; tap off the excess flour and divide the mixture between them. Bake in a pre-heated, moderate oven, on a shelf above the centre of the oven, for approximately 20 minutes, or until firm to the touch. Turn out and sandwich together with jam, or mock cream, or both.

An 'egg ' is a good raising agent for cakes etc, but remember, we do not use egg yolk. To make an 'egg', separate the yolk and the white, - give the yolk to the roses in the garden, they love 'em! Whisk the white lightly and add 1 tspn of baking powder and 1 tspn of vinegar, whisk lightly, using a fork or a balloon whisk, and use at once.

Queen Cakes

Use the same recipe as for the Egg-less sponge, but use only 6 tbspn of Soya milk. Spoon the mixture into a deep greased bun tray, and bake in a pre-heated hot oven for 10-12 minutes. Turn out onto a wire tray to cool.

These are nice iced, but mix the icing sugar with milk or fruit juice, and it will be crisp not sticky.

Perfect Pancakes

½ pint Soya milk or milk and water

1 egg separated, use only the white

4 ozs plain flour

Pinch salt

1 tspn baking powder

Sift the flour and baking powder together, add the lightly beaten egg white and salt, gradually add the milk, beating thoroughly. Leave to stand for half an hour. Heat a small amount of oil in a small frying pan, and pour in enough batter to make a not too thick pancake.

Cook for 1 minute on the first side, ½ minute on the second side and dish up onto a warm plate. Continue until all mixture is used.

Fillings can be sweet or savoury, and are a good user-upper of odds and ends (e.g. fish and parsley sauce, or cooked chicken and tomatoes or the old favourite, lemon juice and sugar).

Ginger and Date Cake

8 ozs self raising flour

1 tspn baking powder

1 tspn ground ginger

4 ozs Trex vegetable shortening

2 tbspn golden syrup

2 ozs sugar

3 ozs chopped dates

4 tbspn Soya milk

Sift the dry ingredients together. Put the fat, sugar and syrup in a saucepan and heat until melted; allow to stand for a few minutes. Mix with the dry ingredients, add an egg white and beat well. Add the milk slowly. The mixture should be of a dropping consistency so a little more milk may be added if the mixture is too stiff.

Line a 7 x 4 inch baking tin with greaseproof paper and pour the mixture in. Bake in a pre-heated oven at 150 C. for 1 hour. Test by inserting a clean skewer into the cake; if it comes out clean, the cake is done.

Easter Orange Fork Biscuits

4 ozs Soya spread

2 ozs caster sugar

grated rind from 1 small orange

5 ozs self-raising flour

Measure the Soya spread into a bowl and beat with a wooden spoon. Gradually beat in the sugar and orange rind then mix in the flour. Flour your hands, and bring the mixture together to form a dough. Break into 16 walnut sized balls and place on 2 greased baking trays. Cook in a pre-heated moderate oven for 10 minutes.

Honey Summer Pudding

There are no particular measurements for the ingredients for this; it was a favourite of my Mother's. It is quick and easy and a good way of using up any soft fruit that may be lurking in the garden or that you may have been given. Any soft or juicy fruit such as raspberries, plums, cooking apples (with cloves) and blackberries will do. The recipe requires no cooking.

Choose a suitable pudding basin, take enough slices of bread to line it. Cut off the crusts, (set these aside for making breadcrumbs), and cover the bread with Soya spread. Line the basin, with the spread side against the basin - line it up, so that there are no gaps for the fruit to leak out of. Having stewed the fruit of your choice, let it cool, then pour it into the lined basin. Take a tbspn of thick honey and lay it on the fruit. If runny, spread or mix it in. Take more bread and spread to make a lid; place the spread side to the fruit. The basin should now be full. Cover with a plate or saucer and place a heavy object on top. (My Mother used to use a flat iron, but a large unopened tin of fruit would suffice, as only a heavy weight is needed). This pudding is best left overnight, turned out and served with cool custard.

Gingerbread

1lb self-raising flour

6 ozs Soya spread

8 ozs sugar

8 ozs treacle

½ tspn salt

4 ozs mixed dried fruit

1½ cups of warm milk

2 tspn ground ginger

1 tspn mixed spice

Rub the Soya spread through the flour. Add the spice, ginger, salt and mixed fruit. Mix the treacle with the warm milk, and stir into the dry ingredients.

Mix to a heavy batter. Grease a 9 inch square shallow tin and bake in a pre-heated moderate oven for 45 minutes.

Sly Cake

12 ozs short crust pastry

8 ozs currants

2 tbspn dark rum

2 tbspn brown sugar

½ tspn grated nutmeg, or mixed spice

½ oz Soya spread

milk to glaze

Put the currants into a bowl and sprinkle them with rum, and stand for 30 minutes. Roll out the pastry and divide into 2, lay half on a greased baking sheet, and turn the edge up all the way round. Spread the rum soaked currants onto the pastry, mix the sugar and spice and sprinkle over the currants. Dot with Soya spread and cover with the rest of the pastry. Trim, and glaze with milk. Bake in a pre-heated oven at Gas Mark 6 – (200 ºC) for approximately 30-40 minutes, or until pastry is golden.

Snow Cake

3 ozs corn flour

5 ozs self raising flour

4 ozs caster sugar

4 ozs Soya spread

½ tbspn lemon juice

3 egg whites

Cream the Soya spread till light and fluffy, beat in the lemon juice. Beat egg whites stiffly, and beat into Soya spread and sugar. Continue beating at high speed for 4-5 minutes. Mix in the flour and cornflour. Grease 2 x 7 ½ inch sandwich tins and cook in a pre-heated moderate oven for 25 minutes.

This cake can be used for a jam sandwich or gateau.

Scotch Trifle

Jam

Snow cake (see recipe)

2 tbspn sherry

4-6 ozs chopped tinned fruit

½ pt custard

Decorating cream

Spread the bottom of a 2 pt dish with a layer of jam. Cover with a layer of Snow Cake (see previous recipe), cut into fingers and sprinkle on some chopped, tinned fruit. Moisten with fruit juice and sherry but do not soak.

Top with a layer of custard made with Soya milk and allow to cool.

Miscellaneous

Glazed Garlic Tofu

1 head of garlic, broken into cloves and peeled

1 tspn red pepper flakes

3 tbspn soy sauce

1 pint vinegar

3 tbspn honey

8 oz block tofu

Blend the garlic, pepper flakes, soy sauce, vinegar and honey in a food processor or blender then transfer to a saucepan and cook for 8 minutes, stirring occasionally until reduced by a third. Cut the tofu into chunks or thin strips, and poach in the mixture for about 4 minutes until the tofu is heated through. The flavour can be varied by adding 'Chinese Five Spice Powder,' toasted sesame seeds, and fresh herbs of your choice. Serve with boiled rice, or fried noodles.

Sausage and Mash with Apple and Celery Sauce

1lb pound of boiled potatoes	1oz Soya spread
1 small onion chopped	1 celery stick chopped
2 red apples cored and chopped	4 Quorn sausages
4 tbspn white wine or apple juice	½ pint chicken stock
½ tspn mixed dried herbs	1 tbspn freshly chopped parsley
small clove garlic peeled and crushed	
4-5 tbspn Soya milk	Salt and pepper

In half of the Soya spread, fry the onion, celery and apple. Cook over a low heat until golden. Remove from the pan and set aside. Add the sausages to the frying pan, cooking until browned (about 5 minutes). Add the wine or apple juice and let it bubble up for a few seconds. Pour in the stock and add the dried herbs, bring to the boil. Return the onion, celery and apple to the pan and add the parsley. Reduce the heat; simmer gently for 10 minutes, reducing the liquid slightly. Melt the remaining Soya spread and fry the garlic for 2-3 minutes; beat in the potatoes, the garlic flavoured milk and Soya spread. Season to taste; reheat for a few minutes then serve with the sausages.

Paella

4-5 ozs cooked chicken	1 small tin of tuna fish
1 large onion	1 clove of garlic
2-3 tomatoes deseeded	1 red pepper
1 tbspn olive oil	2 ozs green peas
1 cup of long grain rice	3 cups of chicken stock
1 ½ tspn turmeric	salt and pepper
1 ½ tspn oregano	

Chop the onion and garlic, rough chop the tomatoes and peppers. Cut the chicken into 1 inch chunks. Flake the tuna; add the oil and all other ingredients. Bring to the boil in a pan, then transfer to a casserole dish with a lid. Cover, and finish cooking in a moderately hot oven (160C) for 20 minutes or until the rice is tender and has absorbed all stock.

Vegetable Paella

1 onion chopped   2 garlic cloves

2 courgettes sliced   1 ½ pts vegetable stock

12 ozs long grain rice   1 tspn paprika

1 ½ tspn turmeric   4 ozs green beans

1 red pepper deseeded and sliced

1 yellow pepper deseeded and sliced

1lb tomatoes skinned, deseeded and chopped

salt and pepper

Put the onion and 1½pt stock in a deep frying pan. Boil for 5 minutes, covered.

Reduce the heat, uncover and simmer for 20 - 30 minutes until the onions are soft.

Add peppers, tomatoes, courgettes, turmeric, garlic and green beans. Cook gently for 10 minutes, then stir in the rice and paprika. Bring the rest of the stock to the boil and add to the pan, cook until the rice is done.

Dumplings

8 ozs self raising flour

1 tspn baking powder

1 tspn sweet herbs e.g. parsley (optional)

cold water

Sieve dry ingredients. Add water gradually, forming a firm dough. Flour your hands and form the dough into balls. Drop into boiling soup or stew and cook for 5-7 minutes. These are fatless and good in a low fat diet.

To make traditional dumplings, rub into the flour 3ozs of Trex then add the baking powder and cook for 10 minutes.

Herb Dumplings

4 ozs plain flour

1 tspn baking powder

2 ozs Soya spread

1 tspn mixed dried herbs

salt

4 fl ozs water

Sift the flour, baking powder and salt together. Rub the Soya spread into the flour until it is like breadcrumbs, then mix in herbs. Add enough water to make a very soft dough. Shape the mixture into small balls and add to boiling soups, stews or vegetables, for the last 30 minutes of cooking time.

Mushrooms a la Provencal

4 good-sized mushrooms, sliced

½ oz Soya spread

clove garlic

Soya milk to cover

1 tspn flour or cornflour

1dspn parsley

Melt ½ oz Soya spread in a small saucepan then add 4 good-sized sliced mushrooms, a clove of garlic, crushed or finely chopped, and Soya milk to almost cover. Cook until tender and add a dspn of finely chopped parsley. Thicken with a tspn of flour or cornflour, stirring constantly.

Cook until thick and then season to taste. Serve on hot toast spread with Soya spread.

This is a filling breakfast or supper dish. It serves 1 and, accompanied by a bowl of soup, makes a good lunch.

Chilli con Carne

8ozs Soya mince

14 oz tin red kidney beans   8 oz tin sweetcorn

1 onion chopped   1 clove of garlic, crushed

6 fl oz water   14 oz tin of tomatoes

1 tspn of oregano   ½ tspn ground cumin

½ tspn paprika   2 tbspn olive oil

1 red pepper, deseeded and chopped

2 green chillies, deseeded and sliced

1 green pepper, deseeded and chopped

Place 2 tbspn of olive oil in a saucepan and cook the onion until golden. Add the Soya mince, red and green peppers and garlic, and cook until tender, stirring gently. Add the remaining ingredients, including chillies to taste; stir, cover and simmer for 45 minutes. This will serve 4 people.

Spaghetti Bolognese

12 ozs spaghetti	1 oz Soya spread

6 ozs lentils cooked in plenty of water until tender

1 large onion peeled and sliced

2 tbspn oil	1 clove garlic, crushed
4 ozs carrot diced	2 tbspn tomato puree
2 tbspn chopped parsley	salt and pepper

To make the sauce, drain the lentils, reserving the liquid. Fry the onion in a medium saucepan for 5 minutes, allowing it to brown lightly, then add the garlic and carrot, and cook gently for about 15 minutes until the vegetables are tender. Stir in the lentils, tomato puree, parsley and a little of the reserved lentil liquid, to give a thick, moist consistency. About 10 minutes before the sauce is ready, cook the spaghetti in a large saucepan until al dente. Drain well and return to the still-warm pan, with the Soya.

Check that the spaghetti and sauce are really hot and turn out on a large warmed serving dish and pour the sauce on top. Offer grated Soya cheese as a topping.

Safflower Oil Mayonnaise

2 tbspn Soya flour

6 tbspn of water

½ pt safflower oil, or any polyunsaturated oil

Blend flour and water to a paste, add oil slowly, a drop at a time, gradually increasing to a tspn at a time, until mayonnaise starts to thicken. Then add oil at a faster rate, whisking throughout the whole process.

Salad Dressing

1 tbspn Soya flour   3 tbspn water

1 pint oil e.g. sunflower or corn oil

Mix together the Soya flour and water to form a paste. Place the measured oil in a jug and pour carefully drop by drop into the paste. Whisk it until the mixture begins to thicken. Oil can now be added faster. Add a pinch of salt and store in a covered container in the fridge. Give the container a good shake before use if the dressing has separated.

Salad Cream

1 rounded tbspn Soya flour   2 tbspn boiling water

4 tbspn olive oil   1 tspn English mustard

½ tspn lemon juice or vinegar   Salt

Mix the milk, flour, salt and mustard with the boiling water. Beat in 1 tbspn olive oil. Mix in the lemon juice or vinegar. Beat in the remaining oil in a thin trickle. (Never pour faster than this or the cream may separate). Check the seasoning. If you prefer the cream thinner, add a tspn of water or vinegar.   This salad cream improves by being kept overnight and will stand without curdling for up to a week. Store in a covered jar but not in the fridge.

Tea Wine

4 tbspn tea

2 ½ lbs sugar

2 tspn citric acid

1 gallon boiling water

Yeast and nutrient

Put the tea and sugar into a white plastic bucket, and pour the boiling water over this. Stir well and infuse until cool. Strain into a demi-john, add the yeast and nutrient, and top up with cold water to the base of the neck. Fit an airlock. When it has finished bubbling it can be bottled.

One small sachet of yeast is sufficient, but I buy a packet of several sachets in the supermarket.

Tomato Sauce for Pasta

2 tbspn olive oil

1 chopped onion

1-2 cloves of garlic, crushed

4-5 tomatoes deseeded (or tin of same)

2 tbspn of tomato paste

Heat the oil in a pan. Chop the onion and sauté until transparent. Add the crushed garlic, tomatoes and tomato paste and stir until reduced and as thick as required.